The Dynamite Book of Bummers

by Jared Lee

A Dynamite Book from Scholastic Book Services

The Book
You Are Holding
Is 100% Dynamite!

Yes, Dynamite Books come to you from the same
scintillating scribblers and peerless pen-and-inkers who
bring you Dynamite Magazine every month: Jane Stine,
Series Editor; Wozney & Lucik Design, Art Direction; Sharon
Graham, Production Editor; and the whole Hot Stuff gang!

12 11 10 9 8 7 6 5 4   0 1 2 3/8

Printed in the U.S.A.

Welcome to the Dynamite Group Gripe!

If you buy a hot lunch in school and the only hot thing turns out to be the milk — that's a Bummer!

If your teacher wears a big smile when she passes out the tests — that's a Bummer!

When you buy a model and find out the instructions are missing — that's a Bummer!

Misery must love company, for every month more than 20,000 kids send in their own personal pet peeves and secret squawks to *Dynamite* Magazine. Then it takes artist Jared Lee's special brand of lunacy to turn these grouchy grumbles into the crazy cartoons *Dynamite* readers know as Bummers.

Now, here is a king-sized collection of crabbiness, complete with the names of the kids whose complaints were the crankiest! *Dynamite* presents the Best of the Bummers . . . or should we say the worst!

Don't you hate sitting on a bench that's just been painted!

Daraugh Gleason, Westbury, NY

Don't you hate when your mom hollers, "Don't get your shoes dirty," right after you step in a mud puddle!

Tammy Paris, Blair, OK

Don't you hate when you wait at the bus stop and the bus passes you!

Paul Luna, Flushing, NY

Don't you hate when you buy five packs of football cards and you already have every single one of them!

Robert Szilvas, Parma, OH

Don't you hate blowing a huge bubble when no one's around to see!

Don't you hate when a friend pops your great big bubble and it sticks all over your face!

Curt Gress, Livingston, MI

Don't you hate telling a joke and forgetting the punchline!

Don't you hate people who forget punchlines!

Don't you hate when a friend offers you some gum-drops and the only ones left are black!

Don't you hate kids who get the fantastic prizes from gumball machines!

Don't you hate smiling doctors with needles behind their backs!

Don't you hate when you go to the dentist for just a checkup and you find out that you have 10 cavities!

Don't you hate when you make fun of people wearing braces and then the dentist tells you you need them!

Jeff Kline, Hayendon Heights, CA

Don't you hate when nobody notices your braces are off!

Don't you hate when the nearest bathroom is 50 miles away!

Don't you hate when you're 100 miles from home and remember you forgot to turn the water off in the bathroom!

Todd Cole, Nebo, NC

Don't you hate hearing strange noises when you're home alone at night!

Don't you hate having to have a babysitter!

Don't you hate when you ask the barber for a trim, and he leaves you with just one hair!

R. Valanisi, San Jose, CA

Don't you hate when you have to go to school the day after you got a haircut!

Mike Aulicino, Livonia, MI

Don't you hate grown-ups who pinch your cheek and say, "My, how you've grown!"

Don't you hate aunts with slurpy kisses!

Dean Saigeon, Pontiac, MI

Don't you hate to rake leaves when they keep blowing around!
Tim Gallinger, Peru, NY

Don't you hate when you go shopping with your mother and you both forget where your car is parked!
Brenda Brovillard, Jefferson, WI

Don't you hate stepping on a bug in your bare feet!

Juanita Dunnan, Hyattsville, MD

Don't you hate to get up on a rainy morning when you left the window open next to your bed!

Grace Callsen, Keokuk, IA

Don't you hate when your pen runs out of ink in the middle of a test!

Ann Belles, Huntington Beach, CA

Don't you hate when you finish your math, then re-member that you did it the day before!

Joe Sarmiento, Kent, WA

Don't you hate when someone reminds the teacher about homework!
David Larson, Westwood, MA

Don't you hate when you fail a test, and the teacher reads your mark out loud in class!
Faye Huntington, Cooperstown, NY

Don't you hate when your teacher asks you why you were late and you don't have a reason!

Yolanda Preston, Atlanta, GA

Don't you hate when your dog eats your homework and your teacher doesn't believe you!

Danny Bachenheimer, Tuxedo Park, NY

Don't you hate when you raise your hand and then you give the wrong answer! Jeanne Jameson, Berryton, KS

Don't you hate when the only thing you got right on your test was the date!

Don't you hate teachers who smile when they give out tests!

Don't you hate when your teacher takes you out in the hall for a little talk! Wendy Morin, Neenah, WI

Don't you hate when your best friend gets an A and you fail the test!

Theresa Deska, Linwood, MI

Don't you hate when a friend starts to tell you a secret, then stops because she thinks you'll blab it!

Brooks Barton, Mt. Kisco, NY

Don't you hate having to be the turkey in the Thanksgiving show at school!

Don't you hate when even though you've been on a diet they still want you to play Santa Claus!

Don't you hate when you're in a play and you forget your lines!
Scott Donnerstag, L.I., NY

Don't you hate when you walk up on a stage during an assembly and you trip in front of everyone!
Andrea Sugarman, Kenmore, NY

Don't you hate soda that was shaken up!

Mark Christiano, Kings Park, NY

Don't you hate when you tip the catsup a little and it all comes out!

Paul Page, Bennington, VT

Don't you hate taking the last apple out of the fruit bowl and finding out it's plastic!

Don't you hate when you finish a box of cereal and discover you ate the prize! Ted Prager, Edison, NJ

Don't you hate when you buy hot lunch and the only thing hot is the milk!

Dynamite Kid, Pacifica, CA

Don't you hate cold pizza!

Don't you hate when it's time to pull the bandage off your sore!
Tom Henley, Omaha, NB

Don't you hate grabbing something to brush your teeth and finding out it's Brylcream!

David Wilkey, Bluffton, IN

Don't you hate finding just half a worm in an apple you're eating!

David Orsky, Billiville, MI

Don't you hate when the ice cream falls off your cone!

Jeff Jacobs, Independence, MO

Don't you hate when you tell your best friend a secret and the next day it's all over town!

Don't you hate when someone calls you good-looking, then apologizes for thinking you were someone else!

Don't you hate when the boy you like can't remember your name!

Don't you hate when a boy you can't stand falls in love with you!

Grace Escobar, Los Angeles, CA

Don't you hate when you like your best friend's girlfriend! Paul Goodskey, New Hartford, CT

Don't you hate when the girl you have a crush on doesn't even know you exist!

Don't you hate when you give your new girlfriend flowers, and then find out she is allergic to them!

Maria Salewski, Green Bay, WI

Don't you just hate when your boyfriend gives you half a box of candy!

Don't you hate when the last petal of the flower says
he loves you, and then you notice you forgot one!

Roberta Allen, Folsom, CA

WELL THEN YOU
CAN HAVE YOUR
OL' BALL!

Don't you hate when you tell a girl she can't play and
then she throws the ball farther than you!

Randy Chardonneau, Linwood, MI

Don't you hate when your dad changes radio stations when your favorite song is on!

Don't you hate when you're listening to your favorite song on the radio and the disc jockey talks in the middle of the song!

Brian Nixon, Waldorf, MD

Don't you hate when you get a gift in a big box and most of it is just paper!
Todd Scanlon, Miami, FL

Don't you hate when you buy someone a present and they never use it!
Teri Thornton, Lawrenceville, GA

Don't you hate when you're excited about seeing somebody, but they couldn't care less about seeing you!

Don't you hate when someone you never planned to invite to your party gets you a birthday present!

Ann Kirby, Oakton, VA

Don't you hate when you get your little brother a
nice gift and he gives you a hamburger coupon!

Don't you hate when you buy a model and find out
the instructions are missing! Tom Martin, New London, WI

Don't you hate when your mom says, "Yes," and your dad says, "No"!

Lecretia Teems, Bessemer, AL

Don't you hate being punished for things that no one else gets punished for!

George Cundari, Jr., Chicago, IL

Don't you hate when your dad gives you a real long lecture and it's the same one he gave you last week!

Todd Oliverius

Don't you hate when you get blamed for something you didn't do!

Rhonda Burris, McAllen, TX

Don't you hate when you get a neat-o poster and your little brother rips it up! Herbie Rackliff, Mayville, MI

Don't you hate going to a dance with your brother!

Don't you hate when you step on chewing gum!

Sharon Maggie, Spruce, MI

Don't you hate when someone puts bubblegum on your seat!

Don't you hate when you burn your toast!

Terry Parish, Pacifica, CA

Don't you hate hot drinks served in paper cups!

Don't you hate when you want to go out on Halloween as Dracula and your mother makes you go in a clown costume!

Lisa Tauscher, Kent, NY

Don't you hate when you have to go out on Halloween dressed as an Eskimo and it's 82 degrees!

Dennis Fitch, Janesville, WI

Don't you hate when you have to wear boots when you're trick-or-treating in a princess costume!

Patti Gnip, Youngstown, OH

Don't you just hate it when it's cold and you have to wear a sweater over your costume!

Don't you hate when somebody keeps talking while you're reading! Pat Stanton, Charlotte, MI

Don't you hate when the only clean socks you've got are one red and one pink!

Don't you hate being very careful about wrapping up good so you won't catch cold, and some sick slob coughs in your face! Mileah Jordan, Abilene, TX

Don't you hate having a snowball fight and someone on your team throws a snowball in your face!
Rosemary Pongracz, Bethel Park, PA

Don't you hate waking up feeling sick and then finding out it's Saturday!   Catherine Ryan, Staten Island, NY

Don't you hate when it's snowing out and you get up and go to school and find out school is cancelled!
Donna Moyer, Pottsville, PA

Don't you hate when you've dropped all your Christmas cards in the mailbox and realize you forgot to put the stamps on them!

Don't you hate when you send out 20 Christmas cards to your friends and you receive only 3!

Don't you hate when you sit on Santa's lap, and he gets a cramp!

Don't you hate stepping on all the creaky stairs when you're peeking at your Christmas presents!

David Wilkey, Bluffton, IN

Don't you hate when on the day you've been planning to go ice skating it turns summer hot!

Don't you hate when you get a new sled for Christmas and there's no snow!

Don't you hate when the only valentine you get is from your grandma!

Don't you hate when someone sends you a get-well card and you're not even sick!

Don't you hate when everyone is cheering for you to catch a pass and you miss it! Kathy Johnson, Fulton, NY

Don't you hate when you're pitching a no-hitter and it starts to rain!

Don't you hate when the coach can't remember your name!

Don't you hate when a 200-pound tackle sits on you!

Wendy Guadwicz, San Jose, CA

Don't you hate when you hit a home run and find out when you reach home plate you missed second!

Kim Fontaine, Oxford, MA

Don't you hate when you spend an hour making an airplane, and when you throw it, it lands on the roof!

Jim Sousae, Pacifica, CA

Don't you hate going to the movies and some 8-foot giant sits down in front of you! Eric C. Wallace, Reidsville, NC

Don't you hate when you go to a suspense movie and the person next to you tells you the whole plot!

Nora O'Callaghan, Evanston, IL

Don't you hate when you try to be cool and nobody notices!

Don't you hate when your heel breaks off!

Don't you hate being caught passing love notes around in school!
Dynamite Kid, Wilmington, DE

Don't you hate when someone opens your mail!
Darrin Cooke, East Ely, NV

Don't you hate talking to a friend about a teacher and then finding out that the teacher is standing right behind you!

Brenda Ohl, Nescopek, PA

Don't you hate when everyone finds out who your girlfriend is!

Mike Pelton, Poughkeepsie, NY

Don't you hate when your mother makes you get all dressed up for a party and everyone else is wearing jeans!

Don't you hate getting hand-me-down clothes from your older brother that are too big for you!

Alex Zamm, Kingston, NY

Don't you hate when your friends give you a nick-name that you don't like!

Don't you hate when you talk to someone and they say, "What?"

Kathy Curths, Wyoming, MI

Don't you hate when the basketball gets caught in the basket and you can't get it out!

Angela Cannon, Newton, NC

Don't you hate climbing up a tree and forgetting how to get down!

Billy Reinhardt, Vincetown, NJ

Don't you hate having a stupid dog!

Don't you just hate when someone names his dog after you!

Don't you hate when your cat sheds!
Darren Courville, Walcott, IA

Don't you hate when you're walking your dog and he starts chasing a cat!
Don Johnson, Pontiac, MI

Don't you hate when the family dog is everyone's dog until there's a mess to clean up!

Ellen George, New Boston, MI

Don't you hate when your little brother finds your diary and reads it!

Laurie Damron, St. Wyan, MI

Don't you hate when your little brother is bigger than you!

Don't you hate when your neighbor's dog is bigger than you!

Don't you hate when you've spent all day reading a mystery book and find out that someone has torn out the last chapter!

Don't you hate when you ask for a special book and get a different one!

Vonnie Karas, Waldoboro, ME

Don't you hate when your mother cooks a terrific looking cake and you find out that it's for company!

Tony Trinidad, Chillicothe, MO

Don't you hate when your mother makes you give back a twenty-dollar bill your Uncle Jack just gave you!

Renee Henley, Omaha, NB

Don't you hate when you ask your mom for a dog on your birthday and she gets you a stuffed one!

Don't you hate when your dad says you're getting a bike for your 13th birthday and you're only 9!

Tom Metz, Burnt Hills, NY

Don't you hate when your mother tells you not to hold the bag that way because it might break, and you say it won't — but it does! Dana Klein, Ellicot, MD

Don't you hate when your father takes a bath and uses up all the hot water! Floyd Ragland, St. Louis, MO

Don't you hate when you're camping out and your little sister has to camp with you!

Jeremy Wood, Washington, IN

Don't you hate going camping and finding out you left your tent at home!

Gary Mendenhall, Virden, IL

Don't you hate when your mom changes the bird cage with the funny pages before you've read them!

Don't you hate when the only one who will listen to you is the dog!

Don't you hate trying to find something after your mother straightens up your room!

Don't you hate when you surprise your mother by making your bed, and she tells you she has to put clean sheets on it! Marcy Gelb, Plainview, NY

Don't you hate when the phone's always busy when you're trying to reach someone! G. Rude, San Pedro, CA

Don't you hate when the TV station loses the picture during the best part of the show! Mark Kulp, Vandenberg, CA

Don't you hate when you walk a mile to the swimming pool and forget your trunks!

Don't you just hate when your swimming teacher nearly drowns you!   Kathleen Welsh, Williston Park, NY

Don't you hate when you hear a crunching sound when you're looking for your contact lens!

Don't you hate when somebody messes up your hair!

Don't you hate when you're asked a question and someone else answers for you! Jackie Bowker, Danville, CA

Don't you hate trying to take a nap when someone keeps talking to you! Pam Chester, Bridgeton, MO

Don't you hate when you have a lemonade stand and nobody buys any!
Debbie Judd, Jackson, MO

Don't you hate when you send in a million Bummers and *Dynamite* doesn't use one of them!
Don Idman, Jr., Escalon, CA

About the Author

When Jared Lee was six years old, he got sick and had to stay in bed for a long time. To occupy his time, he began drawing cartoons.

Jared isn't sick anymore, but you'd never know it to look at his cartoons! Ever since he graduated from the John Herron Art Institute in Indianapolis, Jared has been scratching out his crazy drawings as one of the nation's funniest cartoonists.

A regular contributor to *Dynamite* Magazine, his work also appears in dozens of magazines, children's books, and all kinds of advertising. Jared lives in Lebanon, Ohio. In his spare time he raises prize-winning Shetland ponies.

Practice Shelf-Hypnosis!

Cast a bright spell over your bookshelves and
turn your book collection from dull to Dynamite!
Collect the complete set of Dynamite books:

Magic Wanda's Dynamite Magic Book

Count Morbida's Dynamite Puzzle Book

The Dynamite Party Book

The Dynamite Book of Top Secret Information

The Dynamite Monster Hall of Fame

The Dynamite Book of Bummers

The Officially Official Dynamite Club Handbook

The Dynamite Year-Round Catalog of Hot Stuff